Wizards Spiders and Castles

Poems by **Celia Warren** and **Wes Magee**

Contents

Illustrated by Martina Peluso and Stefano Tambellini

CELIA WARREN

Here is a Field

Here is a field
where dandelions grow,
where silver sails
when breezes blow.

Here is a field
where butterflies feed,
laying their eggs
on the nettles they need.

Here is a field
where rabbits may run
out of their burrows
and into the sun.

Here is a field
where I may lie
in gangling grass
and gaze at the sky.

Moon Moth

Mad moth,
moon moth,
beating on the glass,
powdering the window pane,
chasing after false moons,
bright in our house;
wingbeat a
pattering of rain.
Mad moth, moon moth,
panic in your wings,
fly far away down the street.
As we draw the curtains,
enjoy darker things;
dance to the true moonbeat.

Worm Safety

This worm wriggled and writhed for a week, to keep himself safe from the black-bird's beak.

The Spiders' Football Match

One spider wears a red kit,
The other wears a blue.
"Have you got a ball?" asks Red.
"A rolled-up fly will do."

They kick with six legs; wave with two,
Their goals are big round webs.
Half-time: they gulp a drink of dew,
The score's One:Nil to Reds.

The wind then whistles through the trees:
Time for the second half.
Red flicks the fly to the back of the web
But that just makes Blue laugh:

"Own goal!" Blue cries. "You've
    blown it, Red!"
"That makes the score One All."
But rain stops play so the spiders shake
Eight hands – and eat the ball!

Pick 'n' Mix Zoo

Marshmallow monkeys,
Crocodile drops,
Red jelly elephants,
Lion lollipops.

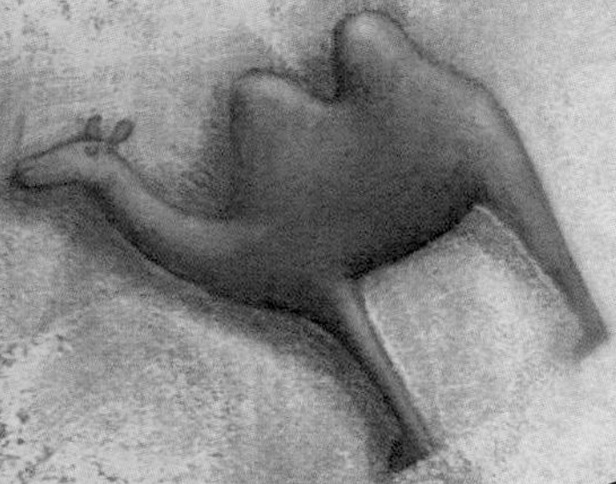

Caramel camels,
Butterscotch bears,
Toffee hippopotamus,
Chocolate hares.

Peppermint pandas,
Candy kangaroo,
Strawberry snakes
At the Pick 'n' Mix Zoo.

9

My Favourite Poem

Chosen by Celia Warren

Some words make me smile and "**jelly**" is one of them. I like the sound and the idea of a "jelly jungle". I also like the way that all the places and creatures in the poem relate to different foods. The poet has used her imagination to create a delightful world that I'd quite like to visit, as the words paint funny pictures in my mind. Her poem makes me wonder what it would be like to live in a swamp of custard and I'd love to meet a sausage-roll bird.

In the Jelly Jungle

In the jelly jungle
Wild beasts and snakes
Make their dens in ice-cream caves
And sleep on chocolate cakes.

In the jelly jungle
The sausage-roll bird sings
Lays its eggs in spaghetti nests
And preens its syrup wings.

In the jelly jungle
The crocodile will doze
In a swamp of custard
With a cherry on his nose.

Jan Dean

Wes Magee

So, you want to be a Wizard?

So, you want to be a Wizard?
    Well, you'll need a pointed hat
    with silver stars and golden moon,
    and perched on top... a bat.

So, you want to be a Wizard?
    Well, you'll need *Ye Book of Spells*,
    six rotten eggs and fried frogs' legs
    to make revolting smells.

So, you want to be a Wizard?
Well, you'll need some pickled brains,
a wand, a cloak, one headless rat
and green slime from the drains.

Do you *still* want to be a Wizard?

The Autumn Leaves

In autumn
the trees wave in the wind
and the leaves come tumbling

down,

down,

down,

down.

Here they come,
hundreds and thousands of leaves
in yellow, red,

hazel,

gold,

and

chocolate brown.

Drink a Glass of Lemonade

Drink a glass of lemonade,
gurgle,
gurgle,
glug.

Second glass of lemonade,
gurgle,
gurgle,
glug.

Third glass of lemonade.
Now you'd better stop.
One more glass of lemonade
and
you'll
go

Pop!

15

In the Castle of Gloom

Oh, it's cold,
it's as cold as a tomb,
and it's dark
as a windowless room
in the Castle,
the Castle of Gloom

        (meet..... your..... doom......)

No sun through the shutters.
No candle flame gutters.
No log embers glimmer.
No silver plates shimmer.
No lamps in the hall.
No brands on the wall.
No moonbeams at night.
No starshine.
No light.

Oh, it's cold,
it's as cold as a tomb,
and it's dark
as a windowless room
in the Castle,
the Castle of Gloom.
    (meet..... your..... doooooooooooooom......)

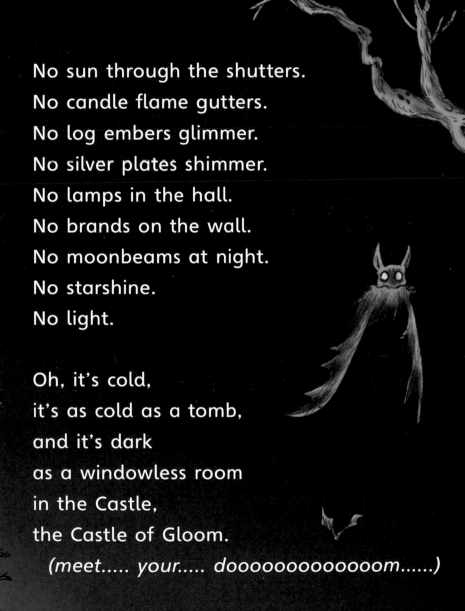

When the Funfair comes to Town

See the coloured lights that flash,
hear the dodgems when they crash,
give the coconuts a bash
   when the Funfair comes to town,
      when the Funfair comes to town.

Smell the burgers, peas, and pies,
wear a mask with wobbly eyes,
throw a hoop and win a prize
   when the Funfair comes to town,
      when the Funfair comes to town.

See the crowds come in and out,
hear the children squeal and shout,
climb aboard the roundabout
  when the Funfair comes to town,
    when the Funfair comes to town.

Taste the toffee you can share,
hear loud music in the air,
ride the Ghost Train......... if you dare
  when the Funfair comes to town,
    when the Funfair comes to town.

The Seagulls

The seagulls glide
above the town.
We throw out scraps
and they swoop down.
One seagull,
two seagulls,
three seagulls,
four!

With a shriek
and a squawk
here come

more,

more,

more!

The Red Boat

There goes the Sun,
slowly sailing by,
like a red boat
on the ocean of the sky.

There goes the Sun,
all the day through,
a red boat sailing
across its sea of blue.

My Favourite Poem
Chosen by Wes Magee

Most of us love swimming but, of course, we can't breathe underwater. In 'Mermaid' the poet imagines what it must be like to live beneath the waves. In just a few lines, and using simple rhymes, he paints a clear and vivid picture of a magical underwater world. When I read the poem I really feel that I am that mermaid who dives deep down to discover King Neptune's secret kingdom and sees all those dolphins guarding his throne!

Mermaid

If I could breathe beneath the sea,
Half person and half fish,
I'd dive down till I found a coral door
And in I'd swish
To swim through weedy canyons
And find the hall of stone
Where Neptune rules the oceans
From his dolphin-guarded throne.

Richard Edwards